Grandma's in the phone!

By Shelby Hoefling

Illustrated by Stephanie Hider

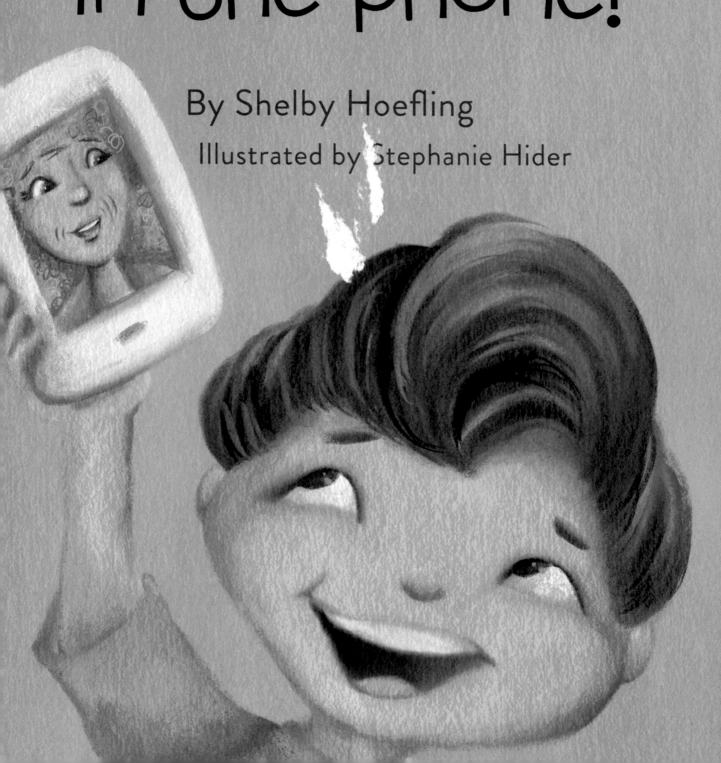

Dedicated to my Grandma, "Nanny."
You have filled my life with love, laughter and joy even when we were
2,500 miles apart. Thanks for always being in my phone! And to Mac,
my nephew with the most fantastic head of hair, thanks for the inspo!
Lastly, thank you to my parents for inspiring me, supporting me, and
simply letting me be me. I love you.

Also dedicated to children and grandmas all over the world,
I hope that you can stay connected in the most meaningful way
possible no matter how far apart.

Mac and Grandma Patty are best friends!
They love hanging out and doing things
together. Everything they do is just a little
bit better when they are doing it together...

The chocolate chips
they bake together are sweeter...

The ice cream scoops they get together are bigger.

And the songs they sing
together sound better.

Mac is so sad when it's time
for Grandma to go home.

"I wish you didn't
live so far away.
I wish we could see each
other and do things
together all of the time!"
Mac says as Grandma
packs up her suitcase.

Mac and Grandma blow each other their special kiss as Grandma gets into her car. Each one catches the kiss before Grandma drives away.

Mac lays in his big green bed at night and dreams about seeing Grandma.

Grandma lays in her big purple bed at night and dreams about seeing Mac.

Sometimes Mac gets to say hello to Grandma on the phone, but it's not the same if he can't see her smile.

He sends her cards, but it's not the same if he can't see her face as she opens his card.

He sings their favorite songs, but it's not the same if they aren't singing them together.

Mac wants to see Grandma and hang out with her. He misses his best friend.

Mac's Mom knows just how to cheer Mac up.

"Mac, would you like to see Grandma and hang out with her this evening?" she asks. "But how can we do that Mom if Grandma lives so far away?" asks Mac.

"With video call the two of you can see each other through the phone and do things together!" Mac's Mom explains with excitement.

Mac starts jumping for joy shouting,

"I CAN SEE GRANDMA! YAY!"

Mac's Mom says Grandma can video call with him when the clock strikes 6:30 pm.

Mac decides to put on his new costume to show Grandma. Grandma might not even recognize Mac! She might think she is getting to video call with a real-life superhero.

"IT IS FINALLY TIME TO VIDEO CALL GRANDMA!"

Mac shouts with excitement.

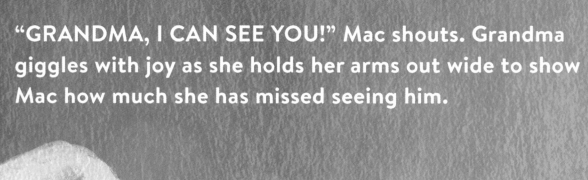

"GRANDMA, I CAN SEE YOU!" Mac shouts. Grandma giggles with joy as she holds her arms out wide to show Mac how much she has missed seeing him.

They both are so excited to see each other and hang out with their best friend!

They sing their favorite songs together and show each other their super cool dance moves as they sing along.

Mac shows Grandma a few things he couldn't show her through a letter or on a phone call.

He shows her a few pages from his favorite books.

He shows Grandma all the funny faces he's learned.

And he shows Grandma what he drew for her that day.

Mac took Grandma to see his new toys and then wave hello to all of Mac's stuffed animal friends.

They missed Grandma too!

They are all so excited to see her that one of them got a little too excited and let out an interesting noise...

Sometimes Mac has to tell Grandma he can't see her. Grandma is pointing her phone's camera at the ceiling fan, not at her face!

Mac wants to video chat with Grandma, not the ceiling fan.

Grandma asks Mac if he can help her with one of their favorite activities they do when they hang out together...

After all, their cookies always taste better when they bake them together.

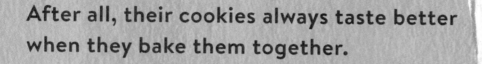

Just
before the
sun goes
down, Mac takes
Grandma outside to
look at the garden that
he and his Mom are growing.
Grandma even got to meet
Mac's friend, Slowpoke the snail!

"Mac time for dinner!"

Mac takes Grandma into the kitchen and shows her what he is having for dinner.

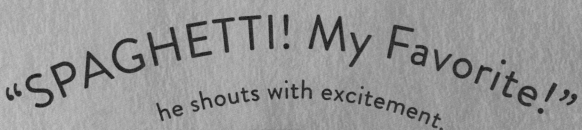

"SPAGHETTI! My Favorite!"

he shouts with excitement.

DING!

Grandma's timer goes off letting Mac and Grandma know the cookies are done.
Just in time before Mac has to wave good-bye to Grandma he can take a look at their masterpiece.

Mac notices Grandma's sneaky cat, Bruno, nearby... uh oh!

It's time for Mac's dinner and for Mac and Grandma to say good-bye.

Grandma tells Mac she loves him very much and loved hanging out with him on their video call.

Getting to see each other brightened their day and the two best friends are happy again!

Mac and Grandma say goodbye to each other and blow each other their special kiss which each catches on the other end. They promise each other to not be sad because they can see each other again and hang out any time despite living so far away from one another.

"Oh, Mac," Grandma added in before Mac hung up the phone, "be on the look out for something special delivered to you in the next few days..."

Mac went to bed that night feeling extra happy that he got to see Grandma. Hanging out with Grandma and getting to see Grandma always makes Mac smile from ear to ear.

Do you like to spend time with your Grandma when she's in the phone? Don't forget to do a few things listed below next time Grandma's in your phone:

HOW TO HAVE THE BEST VIDEO CALL WITH GRANDMA EVER:

1. Tell Grandma what you did today! Did you learn anything you can show her? Tying your shoes? Reading skills? Dance moves? New funny faces you can make?
2. Did you draw anything you can show Grandma?
3. Can you tell Grandma what you're having for dinner?
4. Can you let your stuffed animal friends say hi to Grandma?
5. Has Grandma seen your favorite toy lately?
6. Can you show Grandma your favorite costume?
7. Can you show Grandma what it looks like outside? Walk outside with Grandma to show her the flowers, bugs, the sun, the snow, or some pretty leaves.
8. Do you have a book you and Grandma can read together while on video call? Pick out your favorite book to show Grandma. She'll love it!
9. Are you doing any sports right now you can tell Grandma about? Swimming, baseball, soccer, gymnastics, ballet class... anything!

About the Author:

Shelby Hoefling lives in Northern Virginia just outside of Washington DC. She considers her Grandma, actually known as Nanny, to be her best friend. When living out in California, Shelby had to rely on video chats to stay in touch in a meaningful way with her best friend who was 2,500 miles away. Not only was video chat useful with her Grandma, but she also used it with her nephew Mac. Therefore, the main characters are loosely based on the two people she often always liked to have inside her phone. Shelby also noticed that while video chat is something many children and relatives are experiencing within their homes, there is no children's book out there to teach children how to have quality conversations through video chat nor anything to simply tell a story about what we all are seeing every day! When not taking on the role of a Children's Book Author, you can find Shelby teaching yoga, occasionally to her Grandma, and helping others through Wellness Coaching. Check out her Instagram to learn more!

If you enjoyed the book, please leave a review on Amazon or Goodreads!

Show us your video chat when Grandma is in your phone by uploading a screenshot and tagging us on social media with #grandmasinthephone

Instagram: @shelbyhoefling
Facebook: Shelby Hoefling
Instagram: @stephhider

Please send in your request with who YOU would like to see in the phone next! Mom? Dad? Grandpa? Aunty? Uncle? Stay tuned as there are so many people to be on the look out for in Shelby's Children's Books Series of Who's in the Phone!